G000253596

# TH
# WORK OF GIANTS

*Great Granite Rocks of Cornwall and Scilly*

Peter Stanier

*"One day, friend and stranger,*
*The granite beast will rise*
*Rubbing the salt from his hundred eyes*
*Sleeping no longer."*

Charles Causley

**"THE WORK OF GIANTS"**
© Peter Stanier
First Edition published April 1988
Designed & Typeset by Toni Carver
Produced, printed and published by
The St. Ives Printing & Publishing Company
High Street, St. Ives, Cornwall TR26 1RS

**ISBN 0 948385 10 3**

Cover Photograph by J. B. Stanier: *the author, standing by the giant
pear-drop rock at Horse Point on St. Agnes, Isles of Scilly.*

# CONTENTS

# ACKNOWLEDGEMENTS

I have taken the title of this book from a much admired paper by O. G. S. Crawford, on the stone walls of West Penwith, although the term was used long before by the Anglo Saxons to describe Roman ruins. Important sources have been the writings of William Borlase and Robert Hunt and many others who have felt the magic of the granite landscape. Among these are J.O. Halliwell, biographer of Shakespeare, who turned his attention to Cornwall in 1861, and the naturalist W.H.Hudson who became attached to the area around Zennor in the early years of this century.

I gratefully acknowledge assistance from Roger Penhallurick at the Royal Institution of Cornwall, Truro, the staffs of the Local History Library, Redruth, and the Reading Room and Map Room at the British Museum, London, and many individuals who have, sometimes unknowingly, helped clarify minor points. Acknowledgment is also made to Macmillan Publishers Ltd and Charles Causley for permission to quote from his poem 'Cornwall', published in *Collected Poems,* and to the Royal Institution of Cornwall for the photographs of the Tolmen, Giant's Rock and Luxulyan Boulder, and lithograph of the Logan Rock. The cover photograph is by my father, J. B. Stanier, and that of Dame Barbara Hepworth's 'Rock Form (Penwith)' is by Colin Sanger. The painting 'Giant's Wring' is by Carol (Jasmine) Land and reproduced by permission of the artist. All other photographs and uncredited drawings and maps are my own.

I must also thank Toni Carver, an old climbing companion whose patience has been tried and tested in the quest for obscure boulders on many occasions; his encouragement too has brought this book to fruition.

4

# PART ONE

# CORNWALL'S GRANITE LANDSCAPE

*"The inland parts of the county also present some remarkable*
*objects in the rude mass of granite, in various fantastical forms,*
*which appear above the surface of the moors."*

D. & S. Lysons, 1814

## Geology and Structure

Cornwall's landscape is a hard one in the true sense of the word, and its granite is a byword for strength and durability. Granite is an important part of the geological scene of South-West England, and especially Cornwall. It was emplaced as a fairly fluid magma deep beneath cover rocks of folded Devonian rocks during a late stage of the Armorican mountain-building orogeny, about 280 million years ago. Subsequent erosion of the fold mountain chain has exposed the large granite bosses which now form the high backbone of Cornwall, namely Bodmin Moor, Hensbarrow (St Austell), Carnmenellis and West Penwith. The Isles of Scilly represent the remnants of a fifth boss, 25 miles (40 km) west of Land's End, while the largest of them all is Dartmoor across the border in Devon. In Cornwall, lesser intrusions are found around Carnmenellis at Tregonning Hill, Carn Brea and Carn Marth, while Kit Hill and Hingston Down lie to the east of Bodmin Moor. In addition, there are small outcrops at St Michael's Mount, St Agnes Beacon, Cligga Head, St Dennis, Belowda Beacon and Castle-an-Dinas. The typical landscape of the larger bosses includes rocky tors on hilltops and spurs, their slopes often clothed with a scatter of boulders or moorstones.

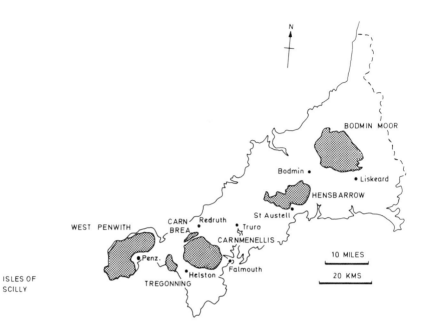

*The six main granite districts of Cornwall and Scilly*

Granite is an acid igneous rock with three main constituent minerals giving the rock its distinctive colour, texture and appeal. Cornish granite has crystals of white feldspars (orthoclase), white or glassy grey quartz, interspersed with shiny black (biotite) and white (muscovite) micas. Tourmaline is an important accessory mineral, found in characteristic black needlelike crystals. Where found in a vein or exposed sheet it is known as schorl. The formation and final sizes of the crystals were related to the rate of cooling and the composition of the original magma. In places, a flow structure is well developed, defined by the long axes of the larger feldspars. Rarely, the crystals may form a cross. Each granite district or boss provides a rock of a different texture. There are even variations within a single district, but in general, West Penwith and Hensbarrow furnish granites with large crystals (phenocrysts) set within a finer groundmass, while Bodmin Moor and Carnmenellis are noted for medium-grained granites.

During a late stage of deep cooling, the granite magma gave off active solutions and volatile gases including fluorine, boron, sulphur dioxide and superheated steam. These entered fissures in the consolidated granite and gave rise to the mineral lodes for which Cornwall is famous. At the same time, some parts of the granite were altered by three main processes. The most important was *kaolinisation,* whereby the feldspars were broken down to kaolin (china clay), by a hydrothermal process or pneumatolysis. There is evidence for this in all the granite districts, although the Hensbarrow granite was the most severely affected and it is here that are found the famous china clay workings to the north of St Austell. China stone is a partially kaolinised granite found in the Hensbarrow and Tregonning districts. The harder varieties can be carved more easily than true granite and have been quarried in times past for local building stone. Kaolinised rocks can be very weak and are a reminder that under certain conditions the apparently indestructible granite is just as vulnerable to decay as any other rock.

By *tourmalinisation,* mica was replaced by black boron rich tourmaline to form a tourmaline granite. Where the process continued and the feldspars were also replaced, a quartz-schorl was formed. This is best seen at Roche Rock, but there are other quartz-schorl dykes on Bodmin Moor at the Devil's Jump and Lanlavery Rocks. One rare form of tourmalinised granite is Luxullianite which contains large crystals of pink feldspar set in a blue-black groundmass of quartz and schorl.

The third process was *greisening,* where the feldpars were replaced by quartz and muscovite. It is especially well developed in the rather weak granite outcrop at Cligga Head.

The jointing of the granite was all important in the creation of landforms and rock features. Near-vertical systems at right angles to each other were caused mainly by contraction during cooling of the granite magma, although some are faults. Horizontal joints include 'pseudo-bedding planes' which may be pressure release joints caused when the cover rocks were removed and the granite slopes roughed out by erosion. Alternatively, they may have developed in relation to the margins of the consolidating magma.

Whatever the cause, they are well illustrated in the main face of Cheesewring Quarry on Bodmin Moor, where they appear to be wrapped around the hilltop 'like the coats of an onion', as one writer has so aptly put it. The joints of the rocky tors on the summit of Stowe's Hill above closely follow the shape of the hill too. The width between the joints of each system varies considerably and this has influenced the rate of weathering and erosion (the closer the joints, the greater the weathering) and, therefore, the resulting landscape forms and the maximum size of detached blocks.

The Cheesewring on Bodmin Moor is probably the most famous tor in Cornwall, being a curiosity as it overhangs all around. Most tors exhibit a tabular nature, where they have been weathered out along the three main lines of joints. The process of the formation of tors is controversial, although it is generally agreed that the initial etching out took place beneath the land surface. Of the two main theories, one has it that the granite was first subjected to chemical weathering when a warm humid climate was being experienced, many years in the past; another sees frost action under periglacial (arctic) conditions to be the cause. However, both theories agree that the jointing controlled the extent of weathering and the final form of the tors, and importantly that the tors were finally revealed when the weathered material (growan) was removed downslope by solifluction during the Ice Ages. Ever since, the exhumed tors have been subjected to the weathering agents of rain and wind. The mass movement of material carried with it the clitters – the detached blocks which now lie scattered on the surface slopes surrounding their parent tors, some showing signs of splitting by frost action. These are the *moorstones,* for centuries sought as a material for buildings and other purposes before quarrying developed in the nineteenth century.

## The Essence of Granite

Wherever it outcrops, from Kit Hill in the east to Scilly in the west, the Cornish granite lends its own strong personality to the county's unique landscape. The most truly granite parts of Cornwall are to be found in the far west. The offshore Isles of Scilly are wholly granite, but on the mainland it is the peninsula of West Penwith where the coarse rock is most evident. The weathered and lichen-encrusted granite make buildings blend into the natural landscape here, far more than for any other rock in Cornwall. The timelessness of the peninsula, with its remarkably rich concentration of prehistoric monuments, is symbolised by this enduring and ancient stone. Some places, such as around Zennor, are one hundred per cent granite.

The granite has of course greatly influenced the everyday lives of the Cornish in activities such as farming, mining and quarrying. In addition, notable and strange granite rocks in the landscape were such obvious features to the people who dwelt nearby that they frequently became associated with a variety of legends and folklore. This was something taken up in the last century by writers such as Robert Hunt whose partly fanciful *Popular Romances of the West of England* makes entertaining reading. He made much of the Cornish giants who were said to have lived among the rocky summits of west Cornwall. The greatest was the Giant Bolster of St Agnes Beacon, who could cross the six miles (9.6km) to Carn Brea in one stride. This feat was depicted in a superb drawing which the artist and caricaturist George Cruikshank made for his friend Hunt's book. He estimated Bolster to have been 12 miles (19.2km) high, but other giants were reckoned to be measured in mere feet. Hilltops or crags with giants include Carn Brea, Carn Galver, St Michael's Mount, Trencrom, and Treryn Dinas. A belief in giants of the past is a recurring theme in folklore, and it is, therefore, hardly surprising that the giants are associated with many large or unusual rocks. The same is true for some prehistoric monuments, arguably as an attempt to explain their existence. Names are preserved, such as the Giant's Castle, Chair, Cradle, Dinner-Plate, Head, Kettle and Pans, and Spoon. Giant's Quoits are widespread and may denote natural or man-made monuments.

We may look upon legends and tales of the giants with mild humour, but they cannot be dismissed entirely for some almost certainly contain the distant folk-memory of actual events. There were other natural stones attributed with magical properties and revered by the local inhabitants. As an example, the Twelve o'Clock Stone near Nancledra would 'rock like a cradle' at midnight but not in daylight, and children were said to have been cured of rickets by being placed on this stone. This idea is repeated elsewhere, such as where children were passed through the holed stone of the famous prehistoric Men-an-Tol in the same district.

All these legends and folklore are underlain by something much deeper, far more sensitive and profound. The granite of Cornwall was once molten and although it has long since cooled and hardened, it still emanates a powerful sense of the living rock, almost brooding. This is not felt by all, some find the granite austere and unattractive, but to those who do it is something difficult to throw off. Prehistoric man must have known it too when he used the stone to build his circles, menhirs and tombs, and it has been felt intensely by many artists, poets and writers who have made Cornwall their place of work. West Penwith has attracted many of these talents, and in describing the district, Ithell Colquhoun aptly observed that,

> 'unless you like granite, you will not find happiness
> there. But if there is that about a granite boulder hung
> with grey and golden lichen which "sends"you, then
> you will feel at home.'

This has got to be true of a district so full of the stuff that you cannot avoid it!

Although the granite is not the most ancient rock in Cornwall, its solidity gives it that sense of great permanence, one that it has been here for all time. Virginia Woolf noticed it, and more recently Denys Val Baker wrote of Cornwall as a granite kingdom, where one is made aware of 'a huge and endless past stretching to the infinite.' D. M. Thomas also used this term *The Granite Kingdom* for his anthology of Cornish poems, which contains his own 'Logan-Stone.' Early this century, W. H.

Hudson captured the feel of timelessness of an ancient land in a stirring description of a winter storm among the rocks and rock basins on Zennor Hill. There are the artists and sculptors too. For example, Dame Barbara Hepworth was aware of the sculptural qualities the Cornish rock forms and indeed the whole of what she called the 'remarkable pagan landscape' of West Penwith. This is reflected in the work she produced since coming to St Ives in 1939, although she chose not to use the coarse and difficult granite, but translated her forms to more easily worked materials such as Portland stone or wood.

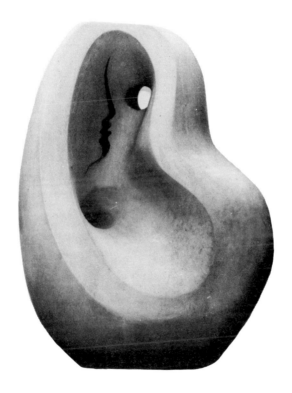

*Dame Barbara Hepworth's 'Rock Form (Penwith)', 1951*

What is it that makes granite what it is? The composition of the granite may be coarse or fine, and the spaces between the jointing may be wide or narrow according to the locality, but all this has influenced its landscape features. Unlike any other rock in southern Britain, it is one of granite's properties that where the rock is solid, it is not easily reduced by weathering. Nevertheless, weathering has etched out along natural jointing so that it is possible to find blocks or boulders of great magnitude: solid, living rock, with few flaws or weaknesses. Subsequent weathering has rounded the angles. Granite crags are common on the coasts and tors of the moorland areas, and at first there seem to be so many rocks to choose from, until after much searching one recognises that there are just a few with really outstanding shapes. These may include features resembling, say a face, an animal or other object, but to me they remain curiosities for they are usually well-jointed. Although not always large, the logan stones must be included for their rocking or 'logging' properties. The most precious are the massive unflawed boulders whose pure shapes lift them far above the rest. The best known of these was the Tolmen, near Constantine, which was literally held on high until it was toppled by quarrymen in 1869. There is something breathtaking about a freestanding monster boulder beautifully sculpted by natural agents, yet so tall it is impossible to climb onto the top without assistance. To myself, this is the very essence of that which makes granite so special over all other rock types.

## Granite Rock Idols

The presence of such an array of weird and wonderful granite shapes in the Cornish landscape could hardly have remained unnoticed and must have had at least some influence on the people who dwelt nearby in prehistoric times. The imaginative writings of eighteenth and nineteenth century antiquarians make interesting reading where they attempt to explain away these rocks as works of art or the druids. Others correctly considered them to be natural formations, but were not adverse to suggesting their appropriation for druidical rites. The great Cornish antiquarian William Borlase had much to say of these 'rock idols'. He described the outstanding examples of the Cheesewring and Tolmen, both of which he considered to have been the objects of worship by the druids. Tolmens were large rocks supported by others in such a way that a person could crawl through the hole beneath, giving them special properties.

*The Tolmen, Constantine (William Borlase)*

A certain amount of aura and mysticism surrounded isolated 'holy' tors, such as Carn Kenidjack on Gumpas Common near St. Just. Borlase refers to this rock as the Hooting Carn, 'probably from the significant prophetic noises which consecrated rocks were supposed by the ancients sometimes to admit.' Carn Brea is

13

another place which has all the ingredients for one of Borlase's druidical temples: a rocky eminence with strange shapes and basins as well as archaeological remains dating back to the neolithic period.

The *logan stone* is a curious natural feature, although not exclusive to the granite of Cornwall. On rare occasions a horizontal joint has been weathered out in such a way that an isolated block becomes pivoted where it remains in contact with the granite surface beneath. The block may weigh many tons but is so delicately balanced that it may be rocked or 'logged' with relative ease, yet not dislodged. Young children or even the wind can perform the task on the best examples. Borlase investigated a number of logan stones in Cornwall and the Isles of Scilly and concluded 'that these are Monuments of the druids cannot be doubted; but what particular use they applied them to, is not too certain.' The most famous one is the Logan Rock itself at Treryn Dinas on the south coast of West Penwith. This was thrown over in 1824 by Lieutenant Goldsmith, but a public outcry caused him to replace it in the same year. Less fortunate was the smaller Men Amber in the parish of Sithney, which was so delicately poised that it could be moved by a child. It was overturned in 1650 by soldiers from Pendennis Castle an event no doubt partly elaborated by the desire to discredit Cromwell's forces in a strongly royalist county.

There are logan stones of all sizes in most of the granite districts of Cornwall. As with many other 'holy' rocks, some have been destroyed over the years by stone masons. Robert Hunt wrote of one such lost example on Tregerthen Downs near Zennor, which an old man of about ninety told him he had 'logged' in his younger days, when the noise could be heard for many miles. Borlase was informed that even the topmost stone of the Cheesewring could once be moved with a pole until the balance was destroyed by weathering. It is interesting that the Ordnance Survey chose to mark some logan stones on maps, naming them in the Old English type normally used to denote antiquities. It is the pity that several of these have been omitted from recent maps. There remain other logans which have never been recorded or marked on any map.

*Rock basins* are found on the upper surface of certain granite rocks in Cornwall and the Scillies. These rounded depressions are the result of natural weathering and erosion processes of frost, moisture and wind acting on a weakened part of the granite surface. The process is slow and the basins may have been initiated in times of severer climate around the end of the Ice Age. Weakly acid water collects in the forming basin and the mica and feldspars are slowly broken down, thus releasing the more resistant quartz crystals. This may be aided by the scouring action of tiny grains of quartz which can be seen being swirled around in the bottom of waterfilled basins on windy days. Some basins are drained by channels, almost as if artificially made, while others have grown and amalgamated to form strange shapes. Among the best examples of these are the Giant's Crocks and Kettles (Carn Brea) and Kettle and Pans on Peninnis Head (Scilly), while King Arthur's Bed on Trewortha Tor (Bodmin Moor) is another.

Borlase, obsessed with his druids, was of the opinion that there were rites of external purification by washings and sprinklings of Holy Water (rain or snow) and that 'these Rock-Basons were vessels most ingeniously contrived to procure that Holy Water.' He noted the stones with basins to be often raised above the ground beyond the reach of cattle or man so they could not be defiled. The highest were so far withdrawn from vulgar eyes ... they had likely a proportionably greater degree of reverence and their waters more holy and more efficacious.' With remarkable confidence, Borlase firmly concluded that the druids used water purifications simply 'because these Basons could serve no other use.' John Wesley was content to believe this when he took a walk on Carn Brea in September 1770, and found,

> 'Druid altars of enormous size, being only huge rocks suspended one upon the other: and rock basons, hollowed on the surface of the rock, it is supposed to contain holy water.'

In more recent times, children and adults were placed in the larger basins of some rocks as a cure for a variety of ailments.

## Granite and Cornishmen

How very poor our surroundings would be without granite, yet it is so taken for granted that you hardly notice it at all! Just look around and see how often man has put this granite to good use and you will realise how important it has always been in the lives of Cornwall's inhabitants.

A rich and impressive store of prehistoric remains is a testimony to man's early recognition that granite was an enduring building material. In the form of moorstones lying on the surface of the land, granite was readily available, but it is the largest pieces which concern us here. Did the builders of these megalithic monuments just choose granite because it was the best material or was there something more, did they too recognise something special about this rock? Did it therefore give some extra religious significance to their monuments?

Very large slabs of granite were chosen for the construction of neolithic *chambered tombs,* known in Cornwall as quoits. The expertise employed in their transport and building can only be wondered at when one looks at tombs such as Trethevy or Zennor Quoit. Although no one stone is very large, bronze age *stone circles* are impressive as groups of stones. They are often enhanced by their carefully chosen sites, in places which may be remote but of great atmosphere. It is a recurring theme in folklore that these are revellers turned to stone as a punishment for hurling or dancing on the Sabbath. Thus, we find the Merry Maidens and Nine Maidens in West Penwith, while on Bodmin Moor there are the Trippet Stones and the triple circles of the Hurlers.

The same explanation is sometimes given for *menhirs,* or standing stones, which are usually much larger. The tallest menhirs in Cornwall today are in West Penwith, but the record one stood in the parish of Constantine (Carnmenellis). It was said to have been 20ft (6.1m) high before being broken up to make gateposts, undoubtedly the fate of many similar monuments over the years. In the same district, there is a tradition that the 10 foot (3m) Longstone has an equal length below ground. However, larger granite monsters can still be seen across the sea in Brittany, a region which has close affinities with Cornwall in culture and granite landscapes.

It was not until the Dark Ages that granite was used again for significant monuments, namely *inscribed stones* and *crosses*. Cornish crosses are widespread and vary from small wayside crosses to larger decorated types. Granite does not lend itself readily to carving, so two carved crosses at Sancreed are of note, while the 8ft 6ins (2.6m) tall Cardinham Cross is perhaps the finest in Cornwall. Outside the granite districts, the St Piran's Cross of the early tenth century stands amid the sand dunes of Penhale Towans, near Perranporth. Any decoration has been worn away by windblown sand.

Since medieval times, granite has been an obvious choice of building material in the districts where it was found, and the readily available moorstones were cut up for building purposes. Many of the remaining boulders around the margins of the granite districts bear the marks of stonecutters: lines of grooves or holes into which wedges were inserted to split the granite. The more prestigious structures requiring granite included bridges and churches. The finest of many notable *bridges* is the white granite New Bridge at Gunnislake, built in about 1520.

Much granite was involved in the rebuilding of *churches* in the fifteenth and sixteenth centuries. Large ashlar blocks in towers as well as the body of the church are seen most commonly on or around the granite districts. As distance increases, granite appears only in piers and arcades or for minor details such as windows and fonts. One must consider the difficulty of transporting such stones, especially in the case of the tall and slender piers within the church. These were often moulded and in one piece, weighing several tons, but the absence of a suitable alternative material made their acquisition and carriage essential.

Much granite, from both moorstones and quarries, can be found in Cornish towns which grew up rapidly in the nineteenth century. As ashlar, lintels or steps, it is all there. It has been used in *houses* and *public buildings* in towns close to the granite, such as Camborne, Helston, Penryn, Penzance, Redruth and St Ives.

There are many notable granite buildings in any of these and other towns. There are few places in Cornwall which do not contain granite *kerbs*. Granite *paving* is less common, but there are good examples to be found in towns such as Helston, Liskeard, Penryn, Penzance and Redruth. There are countless granite headstones and *memorials* in the county's churchyards (although the more easily worked slate is a fierce competitor here), and almost every town and village in Cornwall has its granite war memorial, some of impressive dimensions. Other single granite blocks formed the plinth for statues, probably the best example being the Davy monument in Penzance.

On the industrial scene, *engine houses* feature prominently in the landscape of Cornwall's mining districts, and local granite was a popular construction material. This was not only for walls, but huge flat slabs of granite were often used as bedstones for engine cylinders. A most unusual application of granite was for the so-called 'moorstone boiler', reported to have been used for calcining poorer copper ores near Camborne in the eighteenth century. It was later reused as a boiler for a steam engine at Dolcoath mine. Granite was important for transport systems, and it has been used in many of the railway *viaducts* which span the Cornish valleys. *Ports* have used large quantities of granite for their piers and quays, with Charlestown, Penzance and St Ives being among the best examples. Some of the finest blocks of dressed granite have enabled the rock tower *lighthouses* such as the Bishop, Longships and Wolf to withstand the fiercest storms for a century or more.

Finally, granite has been used for an endless variety of *miscellaneous* domestic, industrial or agricultural purposes. In many ways these are the most interesting, and they include gateposts, milestones and guide posts, apple crushers and cider presses, millstones, staddle stones, rollers, feed and water troughs, tin moulds, etc. These are found almost everywhere, but museums have several items worth seeing and the reader is referred especially to the Lanreath Farm and Folk Museum and the Wayside Museum at Zennor.

It is the purpose of this book to describe some places of excellence in a quest for Cornwall's finest granite rocks, rather than to dwell too much on their legends, religious significance or commercial development. However, it is hoped that the reader will be encouraged enough to follow up these aspects with further research.

*A granite direction stone near Lanivet*

*Jasmine (formerly Carol) Land painted 'Giant's Wring' at the time of the first unaided ascents of the Cheesewring in the late 1960's. This allegorical picture symbolises the relationship of climbers from the Minions Group to the granite of Bodmin Moor.*

# PART TWO

# GREAT ROCKS
# AND OTHER GRANITE PLACES

*"Them ere rocks were put there afore you nor me was boern or thoft ov; but who don it is a puzler to everybody in Sunnur (Zennor). . I de bleve theze put up theer wen these ere wurld wus maade; but wether they wus or no don't very much matter by hal akounts."*

Zennor inhabitant, quoted by Robert Hunt

The descriptions in the following gazetteer are a personal choice of the best granite rock features to be seen in Cornwall and Scilly, progressing westwards from Bodmin Moor. These include remarkable boulders, curiosities and rocky tors, some being famous but others less well known. They all take the visitor to a cross-section of some of the most atmospheric places in Cornwall, which might be peaceful, brooding, or a magnificent high windy viewpoint. Where relevant, some archaeological sites are included. The accompanying maps are simplified for use as a guide only. Grid references are given for the main rock features, so to get the best out of a visit a good Ordnance Survey map is recommended, preferably at 1:25000 scale.

*Note: the inclusion of some sites in this section should not imply an automatic right of access. If in doubt, you should always check with the landowner as a matter of courtesy.*

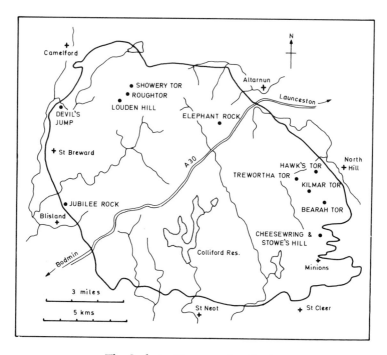

*The Bodmin Moor granite district*

# BODMIN MOOR

Bodmin Moor is the largest granite district in Cornwall and possesses its highest summits. Even the smaller tors are worthy of a visit, although amongst these there are certain rocks, such as the logans, which have a special significance. Stowe's Hill, with the Cheesewring, and Roughtor are the best known and most worthwhile places for the first time visitor.

Man has made great use of Bodmin Moor's granite resource since prehistoric times. There are many stone circles, but by far the most impressive megalithic monument is Trethevy Quoit near St Cleer. This is Cornwall's tallest chambered tomb, standing on a low hill just south of the moor from which the granite was brought for the seven main orthostats and a sloping capstone of about 10 tons. In much later times, river crossings were improved by the construction of granite clapper bridges. There is a small one at Bedrawle across the De Lank river, while Poleys Bridge across the Camel was built with dressed slabs as recently as 1848. The pleasure in these bridges is the way in which great slabs of stone have been utilised in such a crude yet effective way. Some miles distant from the moor, granite is found in the attractive medieval bridges at Respryn across the Fowey and Trekellearn across the Inney.

Large granite blocks have been used for church-building on and off the moors for many miles around. They are usually plain, but St Mary Magdalene Church at Launceston has carvings all over and is a marvellous essay in the carving of granite, that most difficult of materials. This work was financed by Sir Henry Trecarrel in 1542. His nearby manor at Trecarrel was also to be richly worked in granite, but it was never finished and part remains in use as a barn.

The use of granite has been widespread in the towns, but of special note is the facade of Bodmin's early nineteenth century market with its great columns of granite mounted with animals' heads. One can hardly miss the superb 144ft (44m) high obelisk on the Beacon above Bodmin, erected in 1856-7 in memory of Lt Gen Sir Walter Raleigh Gilbert. There is an earlier tall granite obelisk erected in 1771 to Sir Richard Lyttelton at Boconnoc, 6 miles (9.6 km) to the south-east.

### Bearah Tor (SX 259745)

The ridgelike tor lies between Sharp Tor and its bigger brother Kilmar Tor. There is a small quarry on the south side, but the summit rocks have survived. The tallest, just west of the quarry, has rock basins. There are some poor logan stones among the rocks to the east.

### The Cheesewring and Stowe's Hill (SX 258724)

Stowe's Hill, with its great quarry gash on its south side, is a prominent landmark in a fascinating part of the moor near Minions village. The famous *Cheesewring* is a tor near the summit and stands over 20 feet (6.1m) high. Its seven flat slabs set one upon the other, with the smallest at the bottom, give it the appearance of a giant fungus. Tradition has it that the top stone (formerly a logan) turns around once when a cock's crow is heard. Sometimes referred to as the 'Wring-cheese', the name may derive from the stones' likeness to the press used for squeezing out the liquor from the 'cheese' or pounded apples during the cidermaking process. A less preferable explanation is that the stones merely resemble piles of cheeses. The rock basins on the top did not escape the notice of William Borlase, who concluded that,

> 'As the Rock-basons shew that it was usual to get
> upon the top of this karn, it might probably serve the
> Druid to harange the Audience, pronounce decisions,
> and foretell future events.'

While Borlase saw the work of the druids here, Dr Maton more correctly commented in 1796:

'The Cheese-rings, as they are vulgarly named, were probably constructed by nature herself, in one of her whimsical moments'.

Whatever the truth, it is not unlikely that such a curious mass of rocks should have come in for some form of idol-worship in the past. Arguably, this has carried on down through historical times to the present day, for over the centuries visitors have made a pilgrimage to see the Cheesewring. The place was far wilder and remoter than today, with no quarry or mine workings, so the Cheesewring must have been a wondorous sight when approached across the heath from the south. In the nineteenth century, Sunday school outings and learned societies all visited here, sometimes on special excursions on the Liskeard and Caradon Railway which terminated in the quarry below. For example, in 1850 nearly 300 members of the Liskeard Temperance Society took a trip on the railway to spend 'a delightful day' at the Cheesewring. In contrast, when the novelist Wilkie Collins came here in the same year, he was accosted by some Liskeard drunks who were picnicking beneath the rocks! Nevertheless, he was impressed for he wrote,

'if a man dreamt of a great pile of stones in a nightmare, he would dream of such a pile as the Cheesewring...'

It is therefore surprising that the famed Cheesewring came so close to extinction, the fate which befell the Tolmen in the Carnmenellis district. Despite the rocks being protected under the terms of the quarriers' leases from the Duchy of Cornwall, the quarry face came so close in 1869 that supporting stones were erected on one side of the Cheesewring in case the pile should be shaken and topple during blasting operations. The stones are still there, but do not quite touch as may be supposed at first glance. The Cheesewring would return to its even more impressive form if these were removed, but such action might seem foolhardy. An unaided ascent of the Cheesewring is only possible by a skilled climber, but one can get up by stepping on a friend's shoulders (or head!) or by throwing a rope over the top.

Even without the Cheesewring, one would visit Stowe's Hill for its summit rocks with their streamlined shapes and carefully poised boulders. It is an easy climb onto the proper summit, which has small rock basins. Just below the main summit pile is a small overhanging mass, tricky to climb, while beyond this is the rather too accessible *Devil's Chair,* for whoever sits in it becomes a poet or goes mad!

At 1250 feet (381m), Stowe's Hill is a magnificent viewpoint. The bulk of Dartmoor is usually visible across the patchwork fields of east Cornwall, while Exmoor can be seen on clearer days. The vista includes the south Devon and Cornish coasts, the latter as far as the Lizard peninsula. But there is more to see on the hilltop. The tumbled stone rampart of the bronze age Stowe's Pound is well preserved, and careful searching around the rocks will reveal the carved fleur-de-lis boundary marks of the quarrymen. South of the Cheesewring and close to the quarry edge is *Daniel Gumb's Cave.* This is but a remnant of the original 35 foot (10.6m) long slab of granite beneath which this eccentric stone cutter and philosopher made a home for his family in the eighteenth century. The original site, which was destroyed in about 1870, hovers somewhere over the quarry void.

*"The Cheese Wring near Liskeard"* (*J. Allen*)

## Devil's Jump (SX 103800)

There are two impressive outcrops on opposite sides of a valley where it plunges off the edge of Bodmin Moor, two miles (3.2 km) south of Camelford. The tower-like Western Rocks rise vertically for 75 feet (22.8m).

## Elephant Rock (SX 196791)

This is hardly an elephant, but is so-called. It is a pointed rock, about 10 feet (3m) long, almost certainly once a logan but now shifted and perched across a cleft between two large flat slabs. There are basins of all sizes on top with some spilling over the lip of the rock. All around there are some enormous slabs of granite up to 30 feet (9.1m) long and part buried. The site is on the south slope of the Beacon, Hendra Downs, and the Elephant Rock stands out on the skyline when seen from the A30 as it climbs westwards onto the moor from Trewint.

*The Elephant Rock*

## Hawk's Tor (SX 253763)

Hawk's, or Luskey's Tor is a long narrow tor about 20 feet (6.1m) high, with a break in the middle. The horizontal joints are conspicuously close together, resulting in large thin slabs resting on the slopes below. A continuation of the ridge to the west ends at the boulder-strewn Trewortha Tor (SX 244757). At the far end is *King Arthur's Bed,* which is a rock basin large enough for a

27

person to lie in. As a viewpoint, Hawk's Tor over-
looks North Hill village to
the east. The northern
slope drops away steeply to
the Witheybrook, beyond
which is the relatively
rockfree East Moor. To the
south, the great ridge of
Kilmar dominates the
skyline.

*Hawk's Tor.*

## Jubilee Rock (SX 104744)

This great rounded boulder would seem more at home at
Luxulyan, but rises out of the moor on Pendrift Common, just
north of the pretty moorland village of Blisland. While home on
sick leave in 1809, Lt John Rogers carved the rock over as a
celebration of George III's golden jubilee. Carvings include the
figure of Britannia, emblems of agriculture, commerce, industry
and plenty, masonic symbols, and the arms of the king, Duke of
Cornwall, Lord Falmouth, and the Molesworth and Morshead
families. His own family coat of arms was later vandalised. Lt
Rogers and his recruiting party dined upon the rock in honour of
the king entering his fiftieth regnal year on 25th October 1809
(there is some controversy here, as a conflicting report says this
was in 1810, on the completion of the year). A song was written
and sung for the occasion by Rogers. He also engraved verses on a
bronze plaque which was once attached to the rock – since
removed, its position can be located. The carvings, which were
originally painted, were 'restored and amended' in 1859 at the
expense of Lady Molesworth and Lord Falmouth, the owners of
the common. On the top of the rock, the well cut inscription 'VR
1897' refers to Victoria's diamond jubilee. The carvings are
difficult to trace on the lichen-covered granite, but they can be

picked out in the shadow when the sun is at the correct angle.

In 1584, John Norden recorded at *Pendre,* a logan stone,

'so equally ballanced that the winde will move it, whereof I had true experience, and a man with his litle finger will easely stirr it, and the strength of manie cannot remove it.'

The stone was thrown down long ago, but has been identified with nearby Pucklers Tor, a group of rocks also carved by Lt Rogers. Pendrift Common is strewn with other boulders and there are many signs of stone-cutting. It looks down towards the deep gorge of the De Lank river, where a famous granite quarry is still at work.

*Jubilee Rock*

## Kilmar Tor (SX 253749)

Kilmar is the third highest point in Cornwall (1280ft or 390m) and is a dramatic long ragged ridge of granite tors, set on Twelve Men's Moor on the eastern side of Bodmin Moor. It is matched on the south and north by the parallel but lower Bearah, Hawk's and Trewortha Tors. This wild area can be approached via a lane from Berriowbridge to a moor gate on the north-east side, or over the moor from Sharp Tor and Bearah Tor.

This remarkable ridge has many large rocks including a huge leaning tor at the western end. The northern side drops away steeply, but on the south the more gentle slopes are strewn with boulders showing the marks of stone cutting. The Kilmar

29

Tramway of 1858 enabled the product from these moorstones and small quarries to be sent to Looe for shipment. Loading ramps and half-finished shapes can be found where they were abandoned. Just as at Stowe's Hill and Bearah Tor, the summit rocks were protected from the quarriers by a boundary marked by a series of 54 carved fleur-de-lis symbols, most of which can still be found with much patience.

*The leaning western rock at Kilmar Tor (J. Allen)*

Possibly the first recorded rock climb in Cornwall was the ascent of the 'Eastern Turret' by Thomas Bond and a friend on 6th August 1802. His account is worth quoting at length as it reflects the great sense of adventure experienced at that date, for this was then a remote world cut off from good roads, and it was still some years before the development of mining and quarrying and the building of the Liskeard & Caradon Railway. Having ridden over from the Cheesewring on horseback, and likened Kilmar to the Great Wall of China, the expedition party first visited the leaning 'Western Turret.' Next, the two climbers tackled the eastern one: – 'My friend got up the first rock by creeping at full length under the overhanging rock;

and I was under the necessity of several times desiring him, in the most energetic manner, to keep as close as possible; for if the body had gone a few inches further out, it must have slid over the sloping rock which overhung the precipice... In this creeping state he thought he should have broken his watch to pieces, as he was obliged to crawl at full length, there being no possibility, on account of the overhanging rock, of going on hands and knees. Upon trying to get out his watch, I earnestly entreated him to desist, for fear of losing his centre of gravity, for on the left hand was the precipice, and raising his right side ever so little might have been attended with most serious consequences. He took my advice, and by another exertion got far enough in to raise himself on his hands and knees, and then on his legs. I then followed him in the same manner. We then examined the rocks above us, in order to observe the best mode of ascending them. I first made the ascent, and in the uppermost rock, discovered the largest Druidal basin we had met with, and observed it had a lip or channel facing the south. The horrid precipices on either side prevented my getting on top of this rock, as I felt a slight vertigo. I then got down on a lower rock, and my friend ascended the uppermost one, and not finding himself dizzy, got into the basin itself (where I hope he will never go again), and waved his hat to our companions below. I desired him to measure the circumference of this basin which he did with his whip, and found it to be about three feet and a half in diameter...The next thing to be considered was how we should get down again ... and I believe nothing will ever induce me to pay a second visit to the top of this rock.'

### Louden Hill Logan Stone (SX 137804)

Louden Hill lies just to the south-west of Roughtor. At its northern end is a low tor upon which is a flat topped logan stone, about 15 feet (4.6m) long. The marks of stone-cutting show that at least one end has been removed in the past, perhaps to improve its 'logging' qualities as the rock is still delicately poised and can be moved with ease. The spot is little visited, but worthwhile as it provides a good view of the craggy summits of both Roughtor and

Brown Willy. The approach from the Roughtor car park passes through extensive remains of bronze age hut-circles and fields.

*The logan stone on Louden Hill*

## Roughtor (SX 145808)

This is Cornwall's second highest summit (1312 ft or 400m) and also one of its most impressive. Its higher neighbour is Brown Willy, a much wilder place but lacking the superb granite tor formations of Roughtor. These two are Cornwall's true 'mountains', and form long north-south ridges which rise up from the moors when seen from afar. There is good access from Camelford by a lane which ends at a car park by a ford. From here there is easy walking to the foot of the western slopes, across an area covered with bronze age hut-circles and field systems – one of the best preserved examples in south-west England. The final approach to the summit is a steep climb through a jumble of rock slabs like great table tops, resting at all angles.

Parts of Roughtor's summit rocks have been washed bare by weathering, leaving unusual streaks of white granite down their sides. The most southerly tor forms a rocky ridge which overlooks a steep descent. The next is the main summit which has a good *logan stone* with rock basins on its upper surface. It is well worth 'logging', but having observed many visitors at Roughtor, I must conclude that only a few are aware of this stone's magical properties! There was once a small St Michael's chapel here, where there is now a war memorial to the men of the 43rd (Wessex) Division. Among the rocks on the slopes there are marks of stone-cutting as well as abandoned millstones. A bronze age defensive work of tumbled stones can be traced with difficulty in the saddle northwards from the main area to the rocks of Little Roughtor.

*Roughtor's logan stone*

Further north along the same ridge is Showery Tor (SX 149813), a wierd pile comparable to the Cheesewring although not as tall. The topmost stone seems to be a logan, while the remnants of a cairn around the base lends support to the theory that such stones were the object of veneration in times past.

*Showery Tor*

# HENSBARROW

Much of the granite in the Hensbarrow or St. Austell district has been kaolinised, which is the reason for its unique landscape of huge china clay excavations, accompanied by waste tips of white sand. Alas, modern methods no longer produce the old cone shaped tips which earned them the name of the 'Cornish Alps.' An altered granite appears at the well known Roche Rocks on the northern edge of the main clay district. However, the eastern part of the district has a relatively small portion of unaltered solid granite which is characterised by large feldspar crystals.

At the start of the nineteenth century, Richard Polwhele described the land between Roche and Lostwithiel 'where the hills consist entirely of granite or rocks of a granitic nature peeping above the soil in various places, and forming rude grotesque crags.' Today, there are only two tors, at Carn Grey Rocks and Helman Tor, but the parishes of Lanlivery and Luxulyan possess some of the strangest granite scenery in the South West. The mighty natural granite formations of Luxulyan have their counterparts in a spectacular wooded valley setting at Huelgoat, Finistère, in Brittany. There, a stream plunges beneath a pile of enormous round granite boulders, *la Grotte du Diable,* while nearby is a popular logan rock, weighing in excess of 100 tons and aptly named *la Roche Tremblante.* These are on a tourist trail, but Luxulyan is more secretive.

Notable uses of granite by man include the fallen Lesquite Quoit in a field beside a lane one mile (1.6km) north-east of Helman Tor. The capstone is about 16ft (4.9m) long. At the other end of the time-scale is a large plain obelisk at Fowey, just outside the district. It was erected in 1858 to commemorate the landing of Queen Victoria and Prince Albert twelve years earlier.

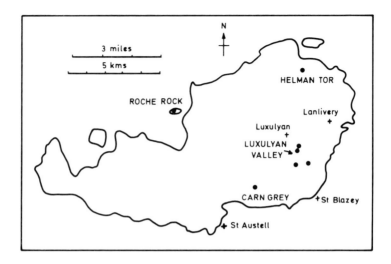

*The Hensbarrow granite district*

Having since fallen into the harbour, it was recovered in 1977 and re-erected in the Caffa Mill car park. To me, its significance lies in its simplicity and the fact that it was fashioned from a single piece of granite.

### Carn Grey Rocks (SX 034551)

A quarry comes right up to the flat topped rocks of this rare small tor. This popular spot near St Austell had been used as a pulpit, 'when a goodly company would assemble,' but fears that it would be lost to the quarry were raised at the time of the destruction of the Tolmen in 1869. It survived, and the summit gives a commanding view out over St Austell Bay.

### Helman Tor (SX 063616)

The abundance of rocks on this atmospheric hill make up for the lack of tors in the rest of the Hensbarrow granite district. Its craggy outline rises to 687 feet (209m) on the western side of Red Moor. A lane gives access at the south end and the new Saint's

36

Way footpath (Forth an Syns) passes this way. Massive flat rocks are a feature of the northern end, while the the main summit pile includes a *logan rock*. This is in an unlikely position, just below the summit on its south-west side. It is shown on the Ordnance Survey map, but at least two others have been recorded here. The hilltop is of archaeological interest as there are traces of a possible neolithic settlement enclosure here, similar to that found on Carn Brea. There is also evidence of much later stone-cutting among the rocks.

*The logan stone (L) among the summit rocks at Helman Tor*

South of the main hill is an isolated rock of great size, the Cup and Saucer Rock. It has all the appearance of a tolmen, being supported in such a way that one can crawl beneath. One of its lesser companions is a logan, and there are also rock basins here.

*The Cup and Saucer Rock*

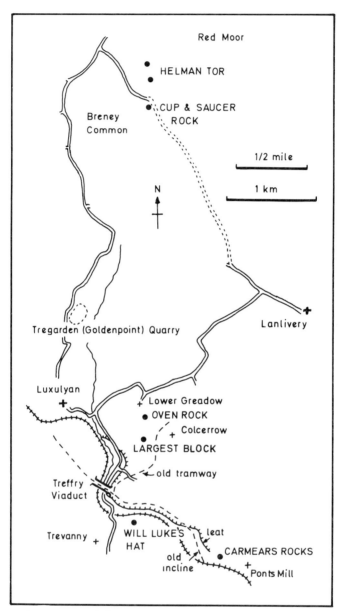

*Helman Tor and the Luxulyan Valley*

## Luxulyan and its Valley (SX 056572)

The whole area around Luxulyan breathes granite, from the massive field boulders to the dressed blocks used in the church and cottages of the granite village. On the rough open slopes, among the trees, and even in the surrounding fields, there are legions of rounded and half-buried granite boulders. Their great size, shape and number make this place quite unlike anywhere else in Cornwall. The woodland in the valley adds to the excitement of boulder hunting, for they loom up out of the undergrowth at the very last minute. Many individual stones are worthy of note, but only a selection is given here. Nineteenth century guidebooks and travellers mention the now destroyed *Whispering Stone or Speaking Rock* at Tregarden Downs, which returned the echo of the slightest whisper. In 1870, a nearby logan rock 'of more than ordinary pretension' was reported to be wedged up with smaller stones to prevent it moving.

The star attraction of the valley must be the reputed *Largest Block in Europe, or Giant Block* (SX 061576), which is free-standing but overhanging considerably on one side. It is a block in its own

*The Largest Block in Europe (left), photographed by Herbert Hughes in 1909*

right, unlike the massive boulders in mountain areas which have broken off from the crags above. The earliest reference for this claim I can find is 1892, when Ward and Baddeley wrote: 'We believe this is the largest block in Europe, larger than any of the famous boulders at the head of the Italian lakes. It may rank with the largest known, the Agassiz blocks, in the Tijuca mountains near Rio Janeiro.' They used the term block 'advisedly,' but in this book I have been less strict in the use of the words block or boulder. By my own measurements, this egg-shaped monster has a length of 50 feet (15.2m) and girth of 75 feet (22.8m), and at a rough estimate weighs 1,700 tons. This makes it far larger than the once famous Tolmen, but it lacks that stone's dominating hilltop position, for it is surrounded by trees on a low spur. There are two other large granite masses nearby, one a tall poised block, and also a group of granite blocks of up to 8 tons each, beautifully squared by masons but never carried away. The site is close to the old smithy and tramway of the famous Colcerrow granite quarries, all now overgrown. The Block and its companions can be approached, with permission, from Lower Greadow Farm. The walk crosses a field of boulders, including the *Oven Rock* which has a very strange hollow at its base.

*The Largest Block in 1978, now surrounded by trees*

*The Oven Rock, Lower Greadow*

*Will Luke's Hat* (SX 060568) can be found in the woods on the west side of the valley, between two quarries. It is a tall mass of granite with a cap, detached from a crag by a deep chasm. It is unclear how this rock got its name, but it may be of relevance that the 1861 Census for Luxulyan recorded a stone quarryman named William Lukes. The two quarries were at work at this time, and from 1867 they were served by the Pont's Mill Tramway.

Anyone wishing to explore the wooded Luxulyan valley and its environs will also be rewarded by the wealth of industrial archaeology. The centrepiece is the impressive ten-arched Treffry viaduct which spans the valley. It was completed in 1842 with huge granite blocks and carried a leat beneath the railway trackbed. One side bears the coat of arms of Joseph Treffry who built the railway system to connect the port of Par with his quarries, mines and china clay works. The course of the tramway and leat can be followed south-eastwards to the top of the Carmears incline which descended to Pont's Mill. Here are the remains of a waterwheel, used for winding until 1874 when the Cornwall Minerals Railway was built through the valley. This became the Newquay branch line from Par, which still passes beneath the Treffry viaduct. The *Carmears Rocks* (SX 069564) rise

41

out of the trees on the east side of the valley, between the incline and Pont's Mill. As with many of the rocks in the valley, this crag is richly clad with mosses and other vegetation. One approach is by following the leat from the top of the incline, before it disappears into a tunnel near the rocks. Formerly, the leat was carried around the face of the rocks on a timber launder and a 200 foot (61m) cascade down the valley side was a popular attraction.

*Will Luke's Hat*

To the geologist, Luxulyan is known for the unique rock known as Luxullianite, specimens of which have large crystals of pink feldspar set in a dark groundmass of quartz and tourmaline. Until a recent discovery of small veins in a granite quarry, it had only been known from an isolated surface rock, the *Hunter's Stone,* in Shabby Rock field on Trevanny Farm. Unfortunately for us, most of this large 70 ton block was cut up and fashioned into the Duke of Wellington's sarcophagus in 1855-6. Steam plant was used for cutting and polishing, and the two men employed in hollowing out the interior had a hard task. Luxullianite is most striking when polished, and the finished article can now be admired in the crypt of St Paul's Cathedral, London.

### Roche Rocks (SW 992597)

A unique and eye-catching group of rocks on open ground, just north of the china clay district and easily reached from the A30 at Roche. The stone is an altered granite (quartz schorl) and its small crystals of white quartz and black tourmaline can be clearly seen. The main rock is about 60 feet (18.3m) high and the ruined fourteenth century St Michael's chapel clings to the south side. The surrounding rocks stand tall with sculpted shapes. In 1602, Richard Carew recorded a rock basin here containing a pool of water which appeared to ebb and flow as the tides.

*Roche Rock*

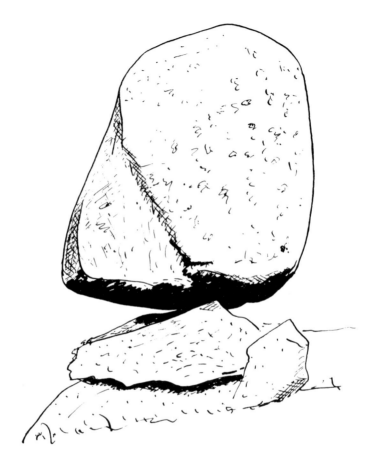

*Poised boulder near the Largest Block, Luxulyan*

# CARNMENELLIS

Carnmenellis is the third largest granite district in Cornwall, yet there are few natural features to be seen. The hill of Carnmenellis is the highest point, at 827 feet (252m), and retains some of its moorland character, but most of the district has been cleared and enclosed. Farming was not the only agent which changed the granite landscape, because stone-cutting and quarrying have destroyed even more in some parts. The increasing demands of the stone trade in the nineteenth century were undoubtedly the cause of the cutting up and removal of the numerous 'moorstones' which once littered the surface of the district. For instance, much of the granite for Waterloo Bridge (1811-17) was obtained in this way before being shipped off from Penryn. These surface rocks were so plentiful that it was not until about 1830 that deep quarrying began on a large scale in the district. Even so, this supply was certainly not exhausted around Penryn in 1862 when it was said that 'the country for some distance round ... is covered with surface granite and roughened by carns, despite the fact that as many as eighty-four quarries were then in operation.'

The larger rocky outcrops, all since destroyed, were marked on early maps. The first edition one inch Ordnance Survey map of 1811 shows Mean Rock, Pelastine Rocks and Black Rock, while R.W. Fox's map of the Penryn granite district (1833) shows Main Rock and Spargo's Rocks. Seven years later, the Tithe Map for Mabe parish includes now vanished rocks at Carnsew, Hawes and Pelastine. The most famous rock, the Tolmen or Maen Rock, must have been an incredible sight before it was destroyed. Lake and Hotten described a large stone on the estate of 'Menhay' (= Menherion?) close to Carnmenellis which was known as the Giant's Quoit and measured about 30 feet (9.1m) long and 25 feet (7.6m) broad. While this was natural, a second Giant's Quoit on Prospidnick Hill was more likely a fallen chambered tomb.

An outlet for all this abundance of granite is expressed in the churches, towns and villages around the district. Among the more impressive granite buildings is Helston's guildhall of 1839, behind which is the granite facade of the buttermarket, now a museum. Cornwall's equivalent to Aberdeen's 'Granite City' is Penryn, which was once the centre of the granite industry to such an extent that a guidebook editor once commented that 'granite is here used for almost every conceivable purpose except as an article of diet.'

### Men Amber (SW 650322)

John Norden, who saw this rock in about 1584, gave the first reliable account of what was clearly a large logan rock:

> 'Certayne huge Stones, so sett and subtillye com-
> byned (not by art, as I take it, but by nature) as a
> childe may move the upper stone, being of a huge
> bignes, with one finger, so equallie ballanced it is;
> and the forces of manie strong men conjoyned can
> doe more in moving it.'

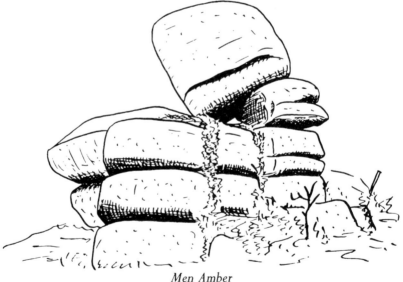

*Men Amber*

He gave its dimensions as 11 feet (3.3m) long and 6 feet (1.8m) high, and produced an illustration showing it as a half-rounded rock with a flat base standing on other rocks. A protruding lever-stone seems to have effected the delicate balance. Of the many suggested origins for its name, Men Amber may be derived from men ambor, or 'stone of fortune', while men ambol, 'rounded stone', is another. Borlase erroneously considered it to come from men-an-bar ('top stone') and that it was an artificial logan erected by the druids. The rock was overturned in August 1650 by a party of soldiers under the command of Captain Shrubshall, the governor of Pendennis Castle. It is now tilted on its side, resting on its supporting rocks in a position little changed since Borlase drew it over 200 years ago.

The site is beside a rough lane, by which it is reached, and looks out westwards from the last high ground of this part of the Carnmenellis granite. John Wesley preached here and the memory is preserved on the spot by a service held every August by the Methodists from Releath.

### Tolmen or Maen Rock (SW 735316)

Although it is no more, this 'Cornish Pebble' was surely the most wondered of all the Cornish granite stones and therefore deserves a full description. Variously known as the Tolmen, Maen Rock or Maen Toll, the name derives from 'holed stone'. The hole, in fact, was beneath it for the Tolmen stood raised up by smaller rocks on a high summit about 690 feet (210m) above sea level in the parish of Constantine. While most impressive when seen from nearby, it was also an important inland landmark for sailors (it can be noted that the sea on both sides of the Lizard peninsula is visible from here). The Tolmen had a length of 33 feet (10m), a maximum width of 19 feet (5.8m) and depth of 14 ft 6ins (4.4m). William Borlase described the whole as 'one vast egglike stone, placed on the points of two natural Rocks, so that a man may creep under the great one.' These supports were said to be only 15 inches (37.5cm) and 5 inches (12.5cm) across at the point of contact with the Tolmen. The top surface was pitted with basins, some of which were connected, leading to speculation that it was a rock idol in prehistoric times. Borlase, who wrote at length on

*The Tolmen, before its destruction in 1869*

the subject, even believed that the major axis lying north to south was proof that the stone had been raised by the priesthood! He estimated it to weigh 750 tons, but Lake and Hotten calculated 'this large orbicular mass' to be about 450 tons. Both the figures have been used by subsequent writers, but my own calculation (based on reported dimensions) puts it nearer 400 tons.

The Tolmen was to go the way of many other natural tors or carns in this major granite quarrying district. The quarries had reached its foot by 1849, when there were fears that it would soon become part of the government works in hand at Chatham and Plymouth. It was suggested that the rock and its pedestal should be purchased, for 'should it be suffered to perish, the disgrace to our native county would never be effaced.' A former proprietor tried to get the London Geological Society and certain Cornish gentlemen to buy the rock from him, but nothing appears to have come of this. Alas, the county was disgraced and the Tolmen was destroyed by quarrymen just twenty years later on the 9th March 1869. Just a few weeks before this event, the landowner Mr Hosken had given an assurance that there was no reason for anxiety when the archaeologist Sir John Lubbock offered compensation after renewed fears for the rock. But the bed of granite beneath the Tolmen was valued at £1000, which proved too much of a temptation for a quarrier named Dunstan, who had been working secretly after dark boring and blasting the rock's supports until the final support was blown out one midday. The Tolmen was thrown off its pivot and hesitated a moment before rolling 40 feet (12.2m) into the quarry below.

The West Briton reported that soon after it had fallen, 'these greedy Goths (quarrymen) fell on it like crows on carrion and commenced boring holes in it intending with their rippers and wedges to split it in pieces.' Within days, workmen were offering small pieces as relics for a few pence to travellers on the Helston-Penryn road. As a tribute, the site of the Tolmen was marked within the quarry on the Ordnance Survey 25 inch map when it was surveyed in 1878. Today, an old timber crane stands in this flooded and long disused quarry. However, in the nearby farmyard at Mean Toll (SW 735315) there can still be seen a strange omega-shaped stone, 11 feet (3.3m) high and seemingly partly worked by hand. It was noted and drawn by William Borlase, who compared it with another on St Mary's, Scilly, and concluded them to be stone-deities, 'their Plint (sic) designed perhaps to express the stability of their God; and the roundness of the upper part his Eternity.'

The Mean Toll Rock

49

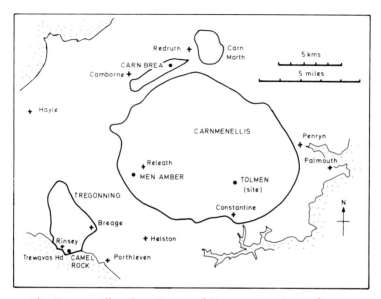

*The Carnmenellis, Carn Brea and Tregonning granite districts*

# CARN BREA

There are two small but significant outcrops of granite just north of the Carnmenellis district. Carn Brea is the distinctive rocky ridge lying between Camborne and Redruth. Although the granite appears to be be separate, it is known to be attached to the much greater body of Carnmenellis at a shallow depth, proven during the working of the Great Flat Lode between the North and South Frances Mines in this rich mining area. However, Carn Marth, which rises on the east side of Redruth, is considered to be an independent intrusion. This hill is more dome-shaped than its narrow neighbour, but it has been much affected by quarrying. Large blocks were still to be seen strewn over the upper part when Dr Berger of Geneva came here during a tour in 1809.

**Carn Brea** (SW 685406)

Carn Brea reaches 738 feet (225m) above sea level, and the fact that it is a good viewpoint and that its granite features are concentrated in a relatively small area make this an excellent place to visit. The central of three summits is surmounted by a conspicuous monument, and the eastern summit has Carn Brea Castle, probably once a hunting lodge but now a restaurant.

Legend has it that the giant Bolster of St Agnes Beacon and a giant who dwelt on the Carn hurled rocks at each other across the intervening miles during a feud. Bolster cleared his hill of granite, throwing most of the stones which now lie around Carn Brea. The summit rocks, however, are said to have been heaped together by the Carn's giant to provide ammunition. The giant is said to be buried beneath his hill and today these rocks provide ample evidence for his presence. When seen from the west, the *Giant's Head* or *Face Rock* (SW 687409) bears a strong resemblance to a face looking out towards the coast and St Agnes

51

Beacon. The rock can be found to the east of the castle, as the hill drops away steeply to Redruth church. Another part of his body, the less convincing *Giant's Hand* (SW 683407), is at the far end of the rock group west of the monument. It is broken in two, but ridges and depressions resemble a hand.

*The Giant's Crocks and Kettles on Carn Brea*

*The Giant's Crocks and Kettles,* or *Cups and Saucers* (SW 684407) is a large mass of granite resting just east of the monument. This the most unusual of all the rocks, as its upper surface is pitted all over with rock basins. William Borlase was fascinated by this rock on 'Karn-bre', and its seven basins falling from one level into another made it in his view an instrument of the druids. In this connection, it is also known as the *Sacrificing Stone.* Beside it is a most impressive piece of granite: a plain but slightly curved slab, 45 feet (13.7m) long and 23 feet (7m) at its widest, like a great whale's back. Borlase also saw evidence for his druids in a canopy-like rock on the south slope below the castle, which he named the *Judgement Rock* (SW 687409). The prominent *Tortoise* or *Elephant Rock* (SW 681406), a short descent to the west of the monument, is so named according to the angle from which it is viewed.

The tapering Monument stands 90 feet (27.4m) high on a square platform on the central summit and was erected in memory of Francis Basset, the first Lord de Dunstanville of Tehidy. It was reported that 30,000 people attended the laying of the foundation stone in 1836. Granite blocks for its construction were quarried from the rocks nearby. There was once a staircase within its hollow interior, to give a fine panoramic view from the top.

There are signs of stone-cutting all over the hill, hardly surprising with the mines and towns of Camborne and Redruth so close at hand. Even back in the mid-eighteenth century, Borlase had noted 'great devastations' among the rocky monuments, and probably the several logans once recorded here suffered the fate of their less exotic brethren. Carn Brea is an important archaeological site too. There are traces of neolithic and iron age defences and huts between the central and eastern summits, although much becomes obscured by bracken in the summer months.

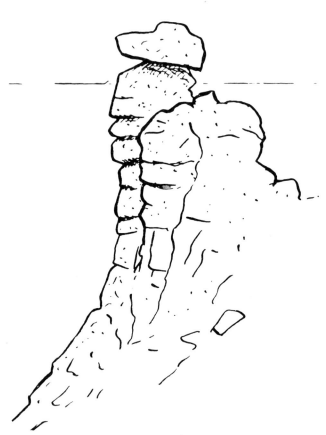

*The Camel Rock from the east*

# TREGONNING

The Tregonning granite forms the two prominent but gently sloping Tregonning and Godolphin Hills which stand like islands above the Cornish plateau-lands between Mount's Bay and the uplands of Carnmenellis. There is a small stretch of this granite exposed along the coast near Porthleven, culminating in impressive cliffs at Trewavas Head. Here is one notable granite formation.

### Bishop, or Camel Rock, Trewavas Head (SW 597265)

Just below the highest cliff top is a detached rock, resembling a bishop kneeling at prayer from the west side, but the head of a camel (or baboon!) from the east. Nearby are two cliff-side engine houses of the Wheal Trewavas copper mine, which was forced to close in 1846 when the sea flooded the workings. These cliffs are best approached from the west along the coastal footpath from the National Trust car park at Rinsey.

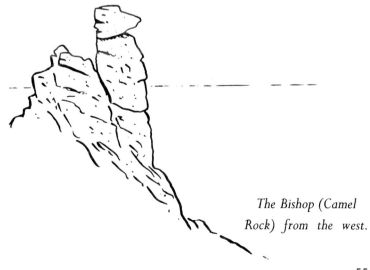

*The Bishop (Camel Rock) from the west.*

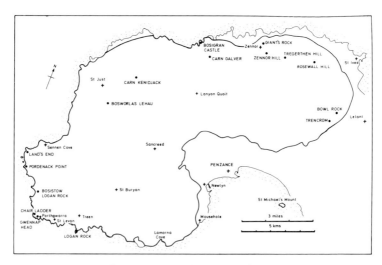

The West Penwith granite district

# WEST PENWITH

This is Cornwall's finest granite district, where the rock exerts its presence everywhere. The natural landscape shows off the granite at its best, with tall cliffs throwing off the forces of the Atlantic, while there are rocky tors on the uplands behind the north coast. The most conspicuous of these are the three craggy spurs of Carn Galver, Zennor Hill and Rosewall Hill, and their rough flanks contrast starkly with the mosaic of tiny fields which carpets the narrow coastal plateau below. In the view of Halliwell, this peninsula was 'anciently the chosen land of the Giants,' something which is easy to believe in a district where so many natural stones have been attributed to giants. There are associations with folklore too, such as the split boulder which has been revered enough to be left alone in its place in St Loy churchyard. It is a tradition that when the gap becomes wide enough for the passage of a donkey with panniers, then will be the end of the world.

Man has always put the granite to good use, and megalithic monuments are everywhere. West Penwith has the tallest menhirs in the county, beside the B3315 near St Buryan. The northernmost of the two Pipers measures 15ft (4.6m), and its equally slender companion is a mere 13ft 6ins (4.1m). Both stones appear to be related to the Merry Maidens stone circle, which is on the other side of the road. The Blind Fiddler beside the A30 to Land's End is another well known example, but there are many more. Lanyon Quoit is the best known chambered tomb, next to the lane across the moors from Madron to Morvah. It once had four supports and was said to have been high enough for a man on horseback to pass beneath, but the structure fell during a storm in 1815. Today, the large flat capstone is supported by just three uprights, having been restored in 1824 with some of the tackle brought to the district for replacing the Logan Rock. It is easy to see why it is sometimes known as the Giant's Table. Away to the north is the Men an Tol, not large but curious for its holed stone. There is a large fallen capstone at Zennor Quoit (see below), and a slightly smaller one at Mulfra Quoit on the south side of Mulfra Hill. Although not so large, granite Cornish crosses are most characteristic of this district, be they in churchyards or the wayside.

To see granite in use in a modern context, Penzance has good granite architecture, with the great pillars of the Market House at the top of Market Jew Street, and the less attractive but large St John's Hall. The railway station also shows the coarse crystalline nature of the district's granite to good effect. St Ives is a thoroughly granite place, with the warm coloured stone everywhere in the old town. Churches here and throughout the district are almost wholly granite, with sturdy towers to withstand the winter gales. The same is true of St Michael's Mount, a tiny outcrop of granite with its priory and castle perched on top. A granite monument worthy of note is the pyramidal Knill's Steeple which stands on the rhododendron clad Worvas Hill above St Ives. This was erected by John Knill, who was a customs collector in the port in 1762-82. He intended it to be his mausoleum, but he died in London and was buried there. A quaint ceremony is held here every five years on St James' Day.

### Bosigran Castle (SW 417369)

The headland can be seen from the coast road east of Morvah and below the ruins of Carn Galver Mine. It is a place much loved by rock-climbers, for an impressive clean face of granite drops over 300 feet (91.4m) into Porthmoina Cove, with its knife-edged island. Across the cove are the Rosemergy cliffs, where the dramatic pinnacled length of Bosigran or Commando Ridge completes the scene. On top of the castle there are traces of defences, and also a flat *logan stone,* about 10 feet (3m) long and easily moved. Halliwell called a large scooped stone nearby the Giant's Cradle. There are good views up and down the coast, from Gurnard's Head to the lighthouse at Pendeen Watch.

### Bosworlas Lehau (SW 378306)

This outcrop of rocks was formerly known as the Giant's Quoits and stands near a small quarry a short distance south-east of St Just. Borlase recorded a logan stone and several large rock basins, but today only the latter still remain.

### Bowl Rock, or Giant's Bowl (SW 522368)

This lonely rounded boulder lies next to a stream and cottage beside the road which skirts St Ives from Lelant to Towednack. It is said to have been rolled here and never recovered by the giants who once played bowls on Trencrom Hill, a short distance to the south-west.

*The Bowl Rock, below Trencrom*

### Carn Galver (SW 425364)

One of the trio of rugged tors along the north coast of the peninsula, this one stands sentinel over Bosigran and Porthmoina Cove. On the summit of this 'two headed carn' is a logan stone, and among the rocks is said to be the cave of the giant Holiburn. Carn Galver is not alone, for a little way inland are the lesser tors of Little Galver and Hannibal's Carn.

## Carn Kenidjack (SW 388329)

This is the mysterious 'hooting carn' of Borlase, so called because of the noise of the wind blowing among its strange rock shapes. The tor stands like a stranded ship in a desolate landscape, and this is a moody and unquiet place in most weather conditions.

## Land's End to Porthgwarra (SW 342250 to SW 372217)

Land's End is the most famous headland in England, and has received many distinguished visitors. Even John Wesley found time to make two visits during his energetic missions to Cornwall. The first time in September 1743, he declared it 'an awful sight,' but he had risen to preach at four in the morning at Sennen, and was to hold four more services between here and St Ives before the day was over! On the second occasion, 25th August 1785, he 'clambered down the rocks to the very edge of the water' at the age of eighty-two. In 1839, Baker Peter Smith was shown a logan stone at the Land's End of an estimated 19 tons. There are also shaped rocks named Dr Johnson's and Dr Syntax's Heads, which are really little more than curiosities. Wilkie Collins could not see Johnson in the former, but found it more 'in violent exaggeration, the worst physiognomical peculiarities of Nero and Henry the Eighth, combined in one face!' Offshore islands include the Armed Knight and Enys Dodman, while closer to Sennen is the Irish Lady Rock.

Unfortunately, Land's End's fame and exploitation makes it difficult to relax and experience the full atmosphere of its granite rocks. But all is not lost, for one can easily escape southeastwards to see the finest granite cliffs in Cornwall along the 3 mile (5.6 km) stretch of coast to Porthgwarra. Pordenack Point has spectacular rocks and finger-like pinnacles, and beyond there are craggy headlands such as Carn Boel and Carn Barra. Between these, at the back of Pendower Cove, is the *Bosistow logan rock*. The property of this stone is said to have been discovered by a man watching for shipwrecks, who was leaning on it when the wind suddenly gusted and moved it. At Chair Ladder (Tol-Pedn-Penwith) there are sheer cliffs of stacked and pinnacled granite, golden with lichen and surmounted by a coastguard station.

*Pinnacles and poised blocks at Pordenack Point*

Finally, there is a logan rock on Gwennap Head. This is, of course, most easily approached from Porthgwarra village and cove.

## Logan Rock, Treryn Dinas (SW 397220)

This most famous of all the logan stones stands high on a rocky support on the dramatic promontory of Treryn Dinas, which also has traces of an iron age cliff castle. The Logan Rock weighs an estimated 65 tons, although some accounts have given a figure as high as 100 tons. Borlase claimed that it was so poised that it was impossible to throw it out of position by any means. By the early nineteenth century, the stone was already a point of interest for travellers and tourists from Britain and Europe, and at least two families made some sort of a living from acting as guides.

The Logan Rock was brought to the attention of the nation in 1824, when Lieutenant Hugh Colvill Goldsmith (nephew of Oliver Goldsmith the author, dramatist and poet) succeeded in disproving the long-held opinion that the stone could never be dislodged. In this he was aided by some of the crew from his 42 ton revenue cutter HMS 'Nimble', on station between the Lizard and Land's End. This was on April 8th, and such was the public outcry that there were even fears for Goldsmith's life, and he was obliged to return the rock to its former position at his own expense. Much of a conflicting nature has been written of these events, but I hope the following is near as possible to the truth.

Goldsmith's own account was written in a letter to his mother about two weeks later. Two ship's boats were creeping along the shore looking for contraband sunk in the sand beneath the Logan Rock (at Porthcurno?), but having finished in the late afternoon and with the wind freshening, they landed to examine the Logan Rock. They were unsuccessful in dislodging it using three hand spikes, so Goldsmith and nine men set the rock in motion, 'which became so great, I was fearful of bidding them try to stop it lest it should fall back upon us, and away it went unfortunately, clean over upon its side where it now rests.' He strongly denied that any instrument had been used, for the *Royal Cornwall Gazette* reported that the men had landed (at Sennen!) with 'ropes, capstans, wedges, etc.' It was also claimed that while this was happening, a smuggling boat had landed part of her cargo along this coast before being discovered. Contrary to a popular belief, the Logan Rock was not thrown off its perch down to the sea, but was dislodged only 3 feet (0.9m) before catching in a crevice. This, however, was enough to destroy its properties and the local guides lost their income. Goldsmith could not have anticipated the outrage he caused and regretted it immediately. He told his mother 'I intend putting the bauble in its place again and hope to get as much credit as I have anger for throwing it down.' In this he proved himself perfectly correct.

Davies Gilbert, being in London, applied to the Admiralty for the loan of machinery to make good this 'indiscrete folly.' He was granted this request and thirteen capstans (one account says six) with blocks and chains were supplied from Devonport Dockyard.

*Replacing the Logan Rock, 2nd November 1824:lithograph published by Tonkin and Vibert, Penzance*

Preparations under the supervision of Goldsmith took many weeks and the equipment was not landed until the beginning of October. Having set up the tackle and capstans, with three pairs of great timber shears and a platform, the act of restoring the rock commenced on Friday October 29th. After a rest on the Sunday, the Logan Rock was replaced at 4.20pm on Tuesday 2nd November. This took place 'in the presence of thousands, amidst ladies waving their handkerchiefs, men firing *feux-de-joye,* and universal shouts.' The total cost came to £130 8s 6d, and a surviving bill gives details of expenses including 13s 6d 'for 60 St Just men who did nothing but drink beer'! Goldsmith was

Goldsmith was saved much of the expenses for Gilbert had begun a fund, contributing £25 at first and later 'most handsomely.' The London Geological Society is said to have given £50. A series of lithographs was published at the time in Penzance and some can be seen in the Logan Rock Inn at Treen. Thus Goldsmith was able to clear his digrace by accomplishing this difficult engineering feat, and a few days later the gentlemen of Penzance gave him a dinner in his honour. On the same day Goldsmith gave his men a 'plentiful dinner' served on the deck of their vessel at Penzance. Gilbert made a second application to the Admiralty to use some of the tackle for restoring the fallen Lanyon Quoit. Again, he started a fund to defray expenses and the work was carried out under the supervision of Goldsmith. The latter did not lose his commission, but was never promoted. He died at sea off St Thomas, West Indies, in 1841.

For some time afterwards the Logan Rock was kept chained and padlocked. When Baker Peter Smith came here in late September 1839, it was still anchored by a double iron chain, but could be set in motion by pulling the chain with one hand. Two wooden blocks beneath the lower end prevented 'overmuch vibration.' The Logan Rock is now free but it can no longer be moved with such ease as before it was thrown over.

### Rosewall Hill (SW 493392)

A broad ridge of a hill lying parallel with the B3306 coast road just west of St Ives, its east and west summits bristling with granite tors and boulders. Those at the eastern end have been called the Cuckoo Rocks. Alas, the *logan stone* here has either ceased working or is very elusive! A short walk past abandoned mine workings (caution required) to the true east summit rewards one with superb views along the north Cornish coast across St Ives Bay to St Agnes and Trevose Heads, inland to the St Austell clay pits, and a glimpse of the Lizard peninsula and the sea on the south coast. The coast road climbs steeply to a saddle which separates Rosewall's craggy western summit from the much lower Trevalgan Hill. This is overgrown, but on the seaward side is a large rounded boulder bearing a simple memorial plaque to the artist Peter Lanyon, who died in a glider accident in 1964.

## Trencrom (SW 518362)

Trencrom, or Trecrobben, is a hill full of atmosphere. The granite walls of an iron age hillfort surround its flat but rocky summit where there are traces of hut-circles too. The hill seems to guard the gateway to the West Penwith peninsula, while overlooking the ancient overland route between the Hayle estuary and Mount's Bay. At the same time, it provides one of Cornwall's greatest viewpoints, with both coasts and the plateau-like nature of much of the county clearly seen. Emerging from this landscape like islands are the granite hills of Godolphin and Tregonning away to the south-east, while eastwards are Carn Brea and St Agnes Beacon, with the more distant outlines of the Hensbarrow china clay district and Bodmin Moor.

Robert Hunt wrote of the 'cyclopean massiveness' of the giant's castle (hillfort) on Trencrom. There is a tradition that the giants who dwelt here buried their gold beneath the rocks, and that this is now guarded by the Spriggans, evil looking creatures of Cornish folklore. Once, a man started searching for the treasure but was scared off before he could reach it. The rocks include the Giant's Chair, Cradle and Spoon, while the Giant's Well is nearby. Halliwell recorded the Twelve o' Clock Stone on the side of the hill, upon which the sun's rays fell in such a way that the shadows enabled the local miners to tell the hour of noon.

## Zennor Hill (SW 461385)

There are rocky tors and boulders all over this prominent hill which towers above the all-granite village of Zennor and gives a good view over the coastal plain with its pattern of tiny stone-walled fields. But first, in an overgrown corner of a field just behind the village towards the sea is the *Giant's Rock* (SW 454388). It is poised on a lower rock, and measures 19 feet (5.8m) long and 8 feet (2.4m) wide, and has good rock basins in its upper surface. It is a logan rock, although its 35 tons could once be moved with greater ease than today.

*The Giant's Rock at Zennor, photographed in 1903
by Herbert Hughes*

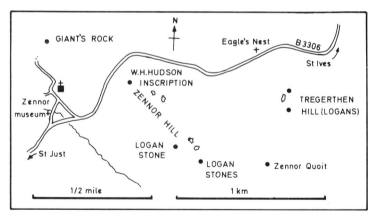

*Granite features around Zennor*

Just above the coast road there are small disused quarry workings on the north slope of Zennor Hill, and a little further up is a sheltered rock from which there is a wide vista. This is where the author and naturalist W.H.Hudson spent much time in contemplation on the occasions he stayed in the village when he was writing his book *The Land's End*. After his death in 1922, the rock face was carved W.H.HUDSON OFTEN CAME HERE. This tribute to his memory was instigated by Will Arnold-Foster who lived at the nearby Eagle's Nest.

There are many large rocks along the summit, and signs of stone-cutting everywhere. Two rocks, perhaps since disappeared, were once known as the Giant's Chair and Giant's Bed. One example which does survive is perched at a steep angle on a smaller rock, and its conspicuous outline is said to resemble a polar bear! Not far from this, and a little way down the west slope is a *logan rock* upon a small platform. It has rock basins (some artificially dammed to help retain water), and its position makes it just the sort that Borlase would have chosen for his druidical rites. This is the logan stone marked on Ordnance Survey maps (SW 463382), but it is a poor one. However, at least two small logans can be found almost at the southern end of the hilltop, and one of these is particularly fine.

*Rocks on Zennor Hill*

Beyond Zennor Hill lies the great burial chamber of Zennor Quoit (SW 469380), which can be approached by following a track to the south-east. The massive capstone is the largest in Cornwall and measures 18ft by 11ft (5.5m x 3.3m). It has fallen and leans against the tomb, which has an inner chamber and antechamber. In 1861, a farmer broke up one of the stones to build a cattle shed and had bored holes in others before five shillings from the vicar of Zennor persuaded him to desist. It is Zennor Quoit to which a local inhabitant was referring in the statement sent to Robert Hunt and quoted at the beginning of this gazetteer. It reflects a delightful innocence regarding these ancient stone monuments, something we have lost in these modern scientific times! While referring to a man-made monument, it seems equally applicable to some of the great natural boulders about which this book is concerned.

Tregerthen Hill lies not far from the quoit, to the north-northeast, and has a scattering of rocks. The granite here is distinctive, with close horizontal joints, and seems to have been the source of material for the quoit. Several *logan stones* can be found. In the nineteenth century, one was called the Cradle because of its shape and a large cavity on top. There are at least two examples of double logans, where the motion of the top stone sets off the one it is resting on.

*On Tregerthen Hill*

# ISLES OF SCILLY

A pilgrimage to the Isles of Scilly is a must for the artist or indeed anyone with an interest in granite, for this is by far the most exciting place for natural granite forms. These all-granite islands (there are nearly 100) furnish some remarkable shapes sculpted by wind, rain and sea, most especially on the southern parts of St Agnes and St Mary's islands.

The northern part of Tresco also has some good rocks, while The Bishop is an aptly named curiosity at Top Rock Carn on St Martin's. In terms of man and granite, the rock has been used everywhere on the islands, from the entrance graves of prehistory to buildings of modern times. However, the most impressive granite structure of all is on St Mary's, where the Garrison Wall required huge quantities of granite blocks when it was built in the first half of the eighteenth century.

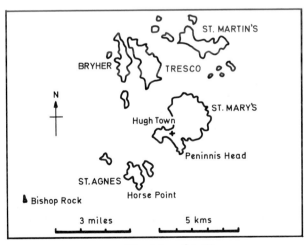

*The Isles of Scilly*

## St. Mary's

The best known and finest headland on Scilly is Peninnis Head,
which Halliwell claimed to have 'the most remarkable specimen
of diversified and fantastic cliff-scenery to be met with perhaps in
the world.' The headland is on the southern tip of St Mary's and
an easy walk from Hugh Town. Upon arrival, one is immediately
delighted by the overwhelming mass of natural sculptures
displayed here. Many have been attributed
names, such as the Giant's Foot, Laughing
Man, Sleeping Bear, Walrus Rock, and
Witch's Head (or Old Witch). The Monk's
Cowl is on the Inner Head. On the
higher ground above the lighthouse
are the *Kettle and Pans,* with
among the largest rock basins
in the West of England. The
*Tooth Rock* (or Elephant's
Tusk) to the south of the
Kettle & Pans is probably
the best known of all
the rocks. Immediately
behind, is Pitt's Parlour
above a steep cliff over
the sea.

*Tooth Rock, Peninnis Head*

The Outer Head is very inaccessible, being surrounded by a
maze of curious rounded cone-shapes known as the *Rock
Labyrinth.* Among these is the *Logan Rock,* over 15 feet (4.6m) high
and computed to weigh 313-340 tons. At one time it could be set
in motion, enabling coins to be bent beneath its weight, but it

later seized up (said to be when a German bomb exploded nearby in 1940). In November 1985, Eddie Prynn and others used hydraulic gear to restore its powers. There is said to be a lesser logan rock of 100 tons in the vicinity. Two prominent rocks on the summit beyond the Labyrinth appear likely candidates, but are not as they are still attached at the base. However, it is worth negotiating the Labyrinth to reach them and admire their impressive size. The outer rock would seem to be unclimbable without aid. At the north-east point of the Head is the remarkable overhanging *Pulpit Rock,* a horizontal 'sounding board' which points seawards like a great gun. For years, guide books have given the length of this slab as 47ft (14.3m), but one wonders who would be bold enough to check it!

Beyond Old Town Bay there are other notable rock features, often indented with rock basins, north-eastwards along the coast as far as Porth Wreck. The Giant's Castle is an impressive promontory anciently fortified as a cliff castle, of which traces of the ramparts remain. Near the edge of the cliff on the west side is recorded a *logan stone* of 45 tons which can be moved with ease, although I confess I was unable to locate it on my search during a time of gale-force winds.

Porth Hellick Bay comes next. On the west side is the *Drum Rock,* a reputed tolmen of the Druids as there is a passage beneath, while opposite is the *Loaded Camel Rock,* a carn not unlike a camel with a load on its back when viewed from the landward side of the cove. This was formerly known as *Dick's Carn,* but took on its new name when the original was destroyed. The *Clapper Rocks* lie to the south-east above Porth Hellick Point and have large and curious rock basins. The coast from here towards Porth Wreck has several points of interest.

The true Loaded Camel Rock once overhung the low cliff at Jacky's Point, although the *Poised Rock* remains here supported by two small pedestals of rock. Just above and close to the coast path is the massive *Sun Rock,* and nearby the much smaller Giant's or Archdruid's Chair from where it is said that the Archdruid watched the sun rise. There is a much more impressive boulder just inland towards the Porth Hellick burial chamber. This is the prominent *Mark Rock,* like a giant football standing about 12 ft (3.6m) above the surface of Porth Hellick Down and unclimbable without assistance. Just below this impressive rock is the lesser Horse Rock which forms a smooth ridge like a horse's back. Close to a footpath across Porth Hellick Downs is the *Basin Rock,* small, but with excellent examples of deep rock basins.

*The Rock Labyrinth at Peninnis Head*

*The Pulpit Rock, Peninnis Head, St. Mary's*

*Mark Rock, Porth Hellick Down, St. Mary's*

## St. Agnes

The south-west side of St Agnes is extremely rocky, with crags and low headlands. There are numerous named rocks in this part of the island, but only the finest examples are included here. The best known and most photographed rock is the fantastic shaped *Nag's Head* which stands alone above Porth Warna, but there are larger and purer forms to the south. On Wingletang Down is the extraordinary *Punchbowl Rock*. There is a basin, nearly 4ft (1.2m) in diameter, upon the upper rock which is perched on a leaning pedestal. Although he did not name it, William Borlase described this as a logan stone in the eighteenth century, stating that the upper rock 'rests on one point only, so nice, that two or three men, with a Pole, can move it.' He considered the whole feature to have been artifically constructed. Just west from here, near Carn Adnis, is an upstanding rock shaped like a pepper pot standing on a flat base.

On the headland above Horse Point at the southernmost tip of the island, there are many granite rocks with their lower parts eroded as if by wind or water, giving them the appearance of mushrooms or bollards. On Horse Point is an apparently unnamed boulder, guarding over a mass of lesser sea-washed brethren. This is the one shown in the cover photograph. It is about 25 feet (7.6m) high and its smooth sides make it impossible to climb. It has a beautifully sculpted pear-drop form and to me, this is the finest of them all. It is aptly situated too, as it looks out across the Atlantic Ocean from the far west end of this last of the granite outcrops of Cornwall and Scilly.

*The Nag's Head, St. Agnes*

*The Punch Bowl on Wingletang Down, St. Agnes*

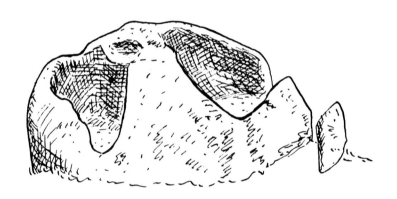

*The Basin Rock on Porth Hellick Down, St. Mary's*

# BIBLIOGRAPHY

I have chosen not to complicate the text with footnotes, so include here the main sources which have provided the background to this book.

Allen, J.  *History of the Borough of Liskeard and its Vicinity (1856)*

Berger, J.F.  *'Observations on the Physical Structure of Devonshire and Cornwall', Trans Geol Soc, I (1811), 93-184.*

Bond, T.  *Topographical and Historical Sketches of the Boroughs of East and West Looe, in the County of Cornwall (1823)*

Borlase, W.  *Antiquities Historical and Monumental of the County of Cornwall (2nd ed 1769)*

Carew, R.  *Survey of Cornwall (1602)*

Catling, R.M.  *'An Unwondered Cornish Wonder Rewondered' (Men Amber), Rep Roy Cornwall Poly Soc, 108 (1941), 68-88.*

Causley, C.  *Collected Poems 1951-1975 (Macmillan, 1975)*

Collins, W.  *Rambles Beyond Railways (1851)*

Colquhoun, I.  *The Living Stones: Cornwall (Peter Owen, 1957)*

Crawford, O.G.S.  *'The Work of Giants', Antiquity, X (1936), 162-74.*

Edmonds, R.  *'On the Tolmen of Constantine', Trans Penzance Nat Hist Soc, I (1849), 309.*

Enys, J.S.  *'Some Remarks on the Granite found near Penryn, and on the Mode of Working it', London & Edinburgh Phil Mag & Jnl of Science, 3rd series, II (1833), 321-7*

Folliott-Stokes, A.G.  *The Cornish Coast and Moors (c1908)*

Gilbert, D.  *The Parochial History of Cornwall (4 vols, 1838)*

Halliwell, J.O.  *Rambles in Western Cornwall by the Footsteps of the Giants (1861)*

Henwood, W.J.  *'President's address at spring meeting', Jnl Roy Inst Cornwall, III (1870), xiv-xv (re. Cheesewring; also council's report, 1869, xli-xlii)*

Hepworth, B.  *Carvings and Drawings (Lund Humphries, 1952)*

Higgins, G.  *The Celtic Druids (1829)*

| Hudson, W.H. | *The Land's End (Hutchinson, 1908)* |
| Hunt, R. | *Popular Romances of the West of England, or The Drolls, Traditions and Superstitions of Old Cornwall (1865 & 1916 editions)* |
| Kay, E. | *Isles of Flowers (Alvin Redman, 1956)* |
| Lake, W. & Hotten, J. C. | *A Complete Parochial History of the County of Cornwall (Truro & London, 4 vols, 1867-72)* |
| Lysons, D. & S. | *Magna Britannia, vol 3: Cornwall (1814)* |
| Mac Lean, J. | *Parochial and Family History of the Parish of Blisland in the County of Cornwall (London & Bodmin, 1868)* |
| Maton, W.G. | *Observations relative chiefly to the Natural History, picturesque scenery and Antiquities of the Western Counties of England, Made in the Years 1794 and 1796 (Salisbury, 1797)* |
| Michell, J. | *The Old Stones of Land's End (Garnstone Press, 1974)* |
| Murray, J. | *A Handbook for Travellers in Devon and Cornwall (6th edition, 1865)* |
| Norden, J. A. | *Topographical and Historical Description of Cornwall (c1584)* |
| Pocock, R. | *Travels through England (1750)* |
| Polwhele, R. | *The History of Cornwall (1803-8)* |
| Smith, B.P. | *Trip to the Far West (1840)* |
| Tangye, M. | *Carn Brea: Brief History and Guide (Dyllansow Truran, 1981)* |
| Thomas, D.M. | *The Granite Kingdom: Poems of Cornwall (Bradford Barton, 1970)* |
| Val Baker, D. | *The Timeless Land: the Creative Spirit in Cornwall (Adams & Dart, 1973)* |
| | *The Spirit of Cornwall (1980)* |
| Ward, C.S. & Baddely, M.J.B. | *Thorough Guide Series: South Devon and South Cornwall (4th ed, 1892)* |
| Ward, Lock & Co. | *A Pictorial & Descriptive Guide to Falmouth, etc (9th ed, 1932/3)* |
| Wesley, J. | *The Works of the Rev. John Wesley, 6 vols (1809-10)* |

## JOURNALS AND NEWSPAPERS

Cornishman, Gentleman's Magazine, Household Words, Royal Cornwall Gazette, The Times, West Briton, Western Morning News

# INDEX